50 Easy Rock Licks

by Alan Warner

Wise Publications *London / New York / Paris / Sydney / Copenhagen / Madrid*

Exclusive Distributors:
Music Sales Limited
8/9 Frith Street, London W1V 5TZ, England.
Music Sales Pty Limited
120 Rothschild Avenue, Rosebery, NSW 2018, Australia.
Music Sales Corporation
257 Park Avenue South, New York, NY10010,
United States of America.

Order No. AM92034
ISBN 0-7119-4160-2
This book © Copyright 1995 by Wise Publications.

Cover design by Michael Bell Design.
Book design by Niche.
Written by Alan Warner.
Edited by Pat Conway.
Music processed by Seton Music Graphics.
Photographs courtesy of London Features International.

Your Guarantee of Quality:
As publishers, we strive to produce every book to
the highest commercial standards.
The music has been freshly engraved and the book has been
carefully designed to make playing from it a real pleasure.
Throughout, the printing and binding have been
planned to ensure a sturdy, attractive publication which
should give years of enjoyment.
If your copy fails to meet our high standards, please inform
us and we will gladly replace it.

Music Sales' complete catalogue describes
thousands of titles and is available in full colour
sections by subject, direct from Music Sales Limited.
Please state your areas of interest and send a
cheque/postal order for £1.50 for postage to:
Music Sales Limited, Newmarket Road, Bury St. Edmunds,
Suffolk IP33 3YB.

Printed in the United Kingdom by
Caligraving Limited, Thetford, Norfolk.

Music Notation And Tablature

The music is written on the upper stave and the tablature on the lines below.

E = 1st string
B = 2nd string
G = 3rd string
D = 4th string
A = 5th string
E = 6th string

This is how the notes appear on the stave and in tablature.
(The number on each tablature line represents a fret number.)

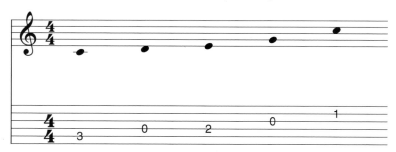

Bars (or measures) divide the music into sections containing an equal number of counts depending on the time signature at the start of the music. (A barline appears at the beginning and at the end of each measure.)

bar
line

bar
line

A 4 over a 4 ($\frac{4}{4}$) at the start of the music indicates 4 counts in each bar and is known as the time signature. There are of course other time signatures, but as we are dealing with Rock music we need only concern ourselves with this one.

Symbols (General)

HAMMER-ON (H)

A hammer-on is where you sound a note as normal then hammer your L.H. finger down hard onto the next note. ⌢H means hammer-on.

PULL-OFF (P)

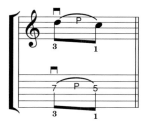

The pull-off is achieved by pulling your L.H. finger down off the string to create the next note. ⌢P means pull-off.

TRILL (TR)

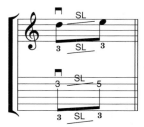

A trill effect is produced by performing hammer-ons and pull-offs in rapid succession.

SLIDE GOING UP (SL)

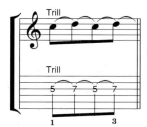

Sound the first note and slide up to the next (higher) note.

SL means slide up.

SLIDE COMING DOWN (SL)

Sound the first note and slide down to the next (lower) note.

SL means slide down.

UPWARD STRING BEND (↑)

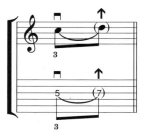

To perform an upward string bend first sound the note, then push string up to raise its pitch. The note in brackets indicates the pitch that the bend should be raised to. An upward string bend will normally be on the 1st, 2nd or 3rd strings. ↑ arrow indicates upward string bend.

DOWNWARD STRING BEND (↓)

For a downward string bend, pull the string down to raise pitch. A downward string bend will normally be on the 3rd, 4th, 5th or 6th strings. ↓ arrow indicates downward string bend.

RELEASE STRING BEND (R)

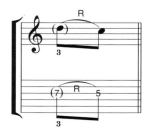

Return bent note back to its normal position after performing a string bend. ⌢R means release string bend.

PRE-BEND (PB)

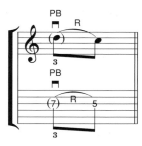

The note is already bent up or down before being struck. When it has been struck you then release so that it goes down in pitch. (The note in brackets is the pre-bent note.)

VIBRATO (〰)

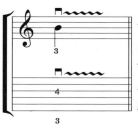

To create a vibrato effect, first sound the note and then rock the string from side to side. A 〰 appears by the L.H. finger number above the note.

The 'Rock' Notes

A lot of rock music is based on just five notes. These notes (or tones) make up the major pentatonic scale (penta = five, tonic = tone). The notes are numbered and are as follows:

1,   2,   3,   5,   6.

The fingerboard chart below shows how these notes appear at the fifth fret. Notice how they fit inside the 'box'. This is known as the box pattern. Although similar in appearance a box pattern is not a chord diagram.

The individual notes may be played in any order to create countless licks.

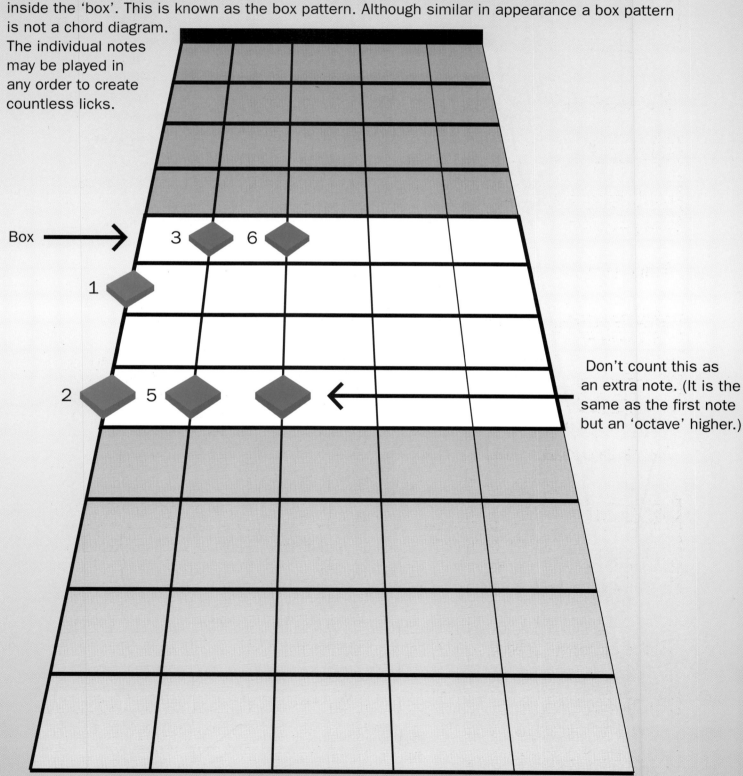

Box →

1

2   5

Don't count this as an extra note. (It is the same as the first note but an 'octave' higher.)

3   6

E Major Pentatonic

Here's the pentatonic scale in the key of E major. This scale, along with the scales which follow, will also have the names of the notes as well as the numbered notes. The notes for this scale are (starting on the open 6th string):

1,	2,	3,	5,	6.
E	F♯	G♯	B	C♯	etc.

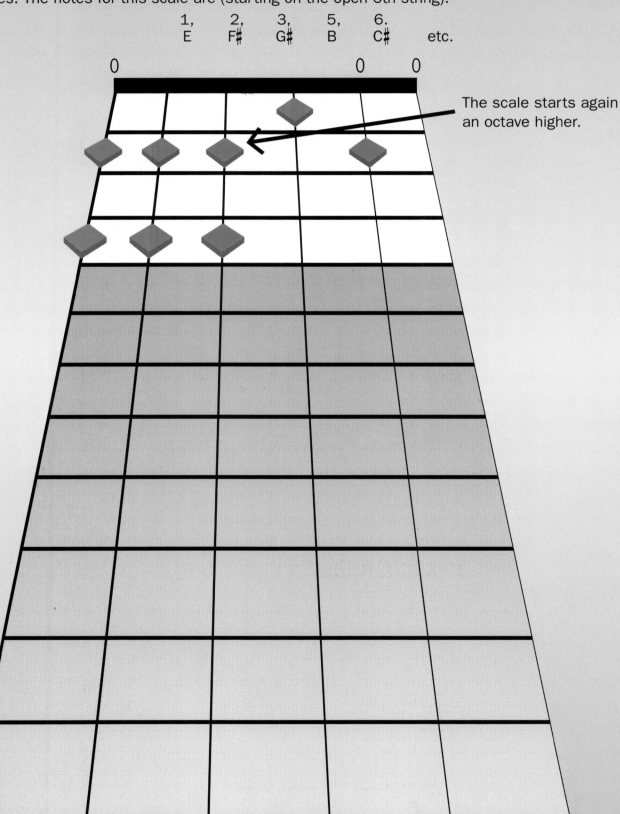

The scale starts again an octave higher.

'BOX PATTERN' LICKS

The following three guitar licks are based on the E major pentatonic scale.

Rock Lick in E

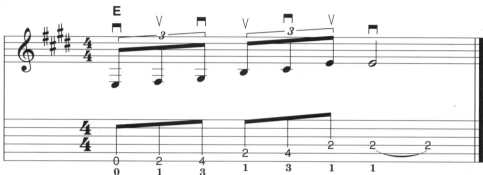

Rock Lick in E

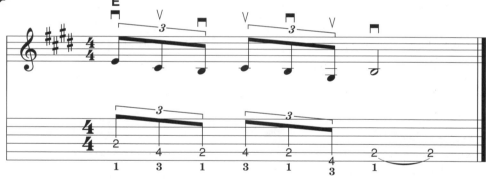

Rock Lick in E

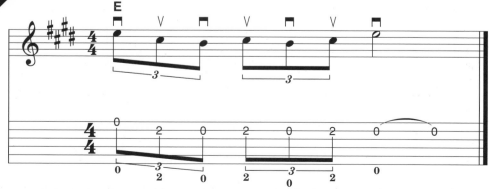

F Major Pentatonic

The notes for this scale (starting at the first fret of the 6th string) are:

	1,	2,	3,	5,	6.
	F	G	A	C	D	etc.

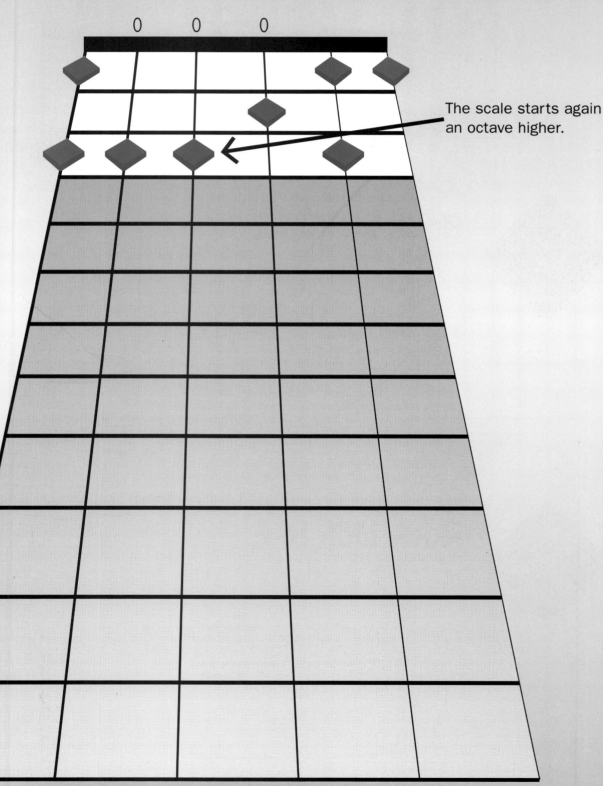

The scale starts again an octave higher.

'Box Pattern' Licks

These three licks are from the F major pentatonic scale.

Rock Lick in F

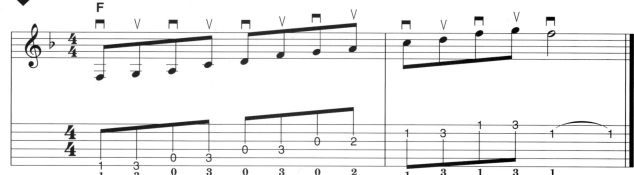

Boogie Lick in F

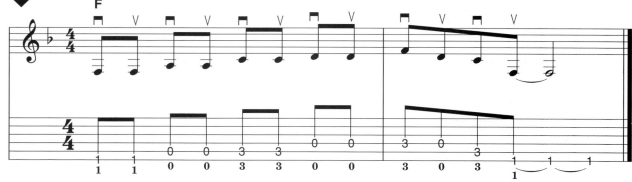

Outro Lick

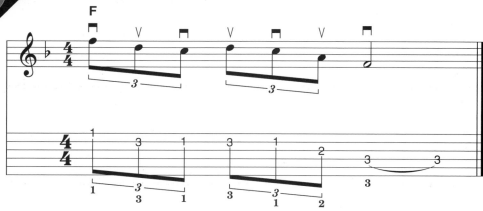

G Major Pentatonic

The notes for this scale (starting at the 3rd fret of the 6th string) are:

1,   2,   3,   5,   6.

G   A   B   D   E   etc.

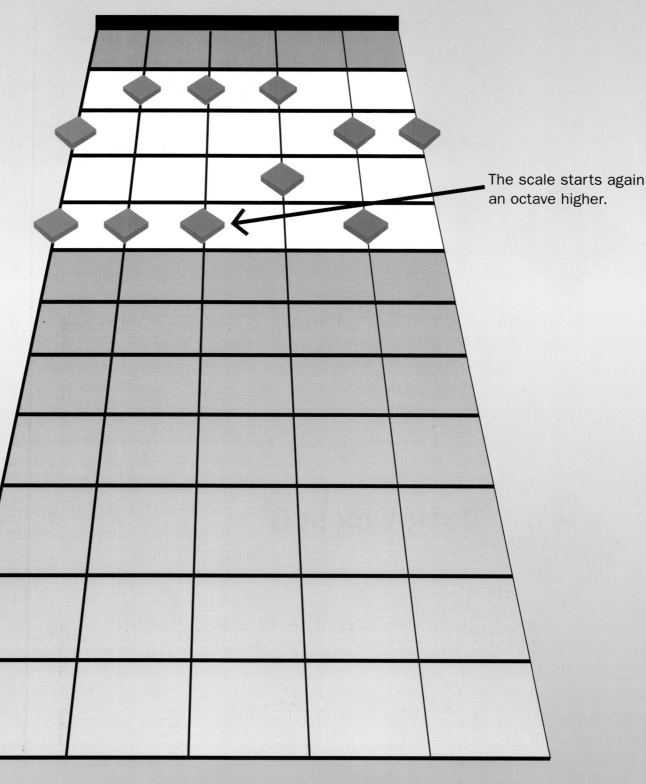

The scale starts again an octave higher.

'Box Pattern' Licks

The following two licks use the notes from the G major pentatonic scale.

Soundgarden

Rock Lick in G

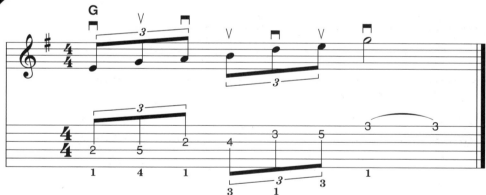

Rock Lick in G

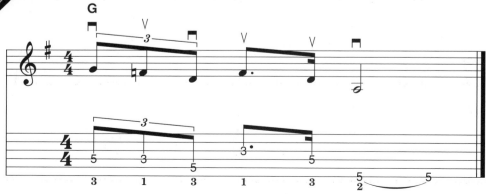

A Major Pentatonic

This scale starts at the fifth fret of the 6th string and the notes are:

1,	2,	3,	5,	6.
A	B	C#	E	F# etc.

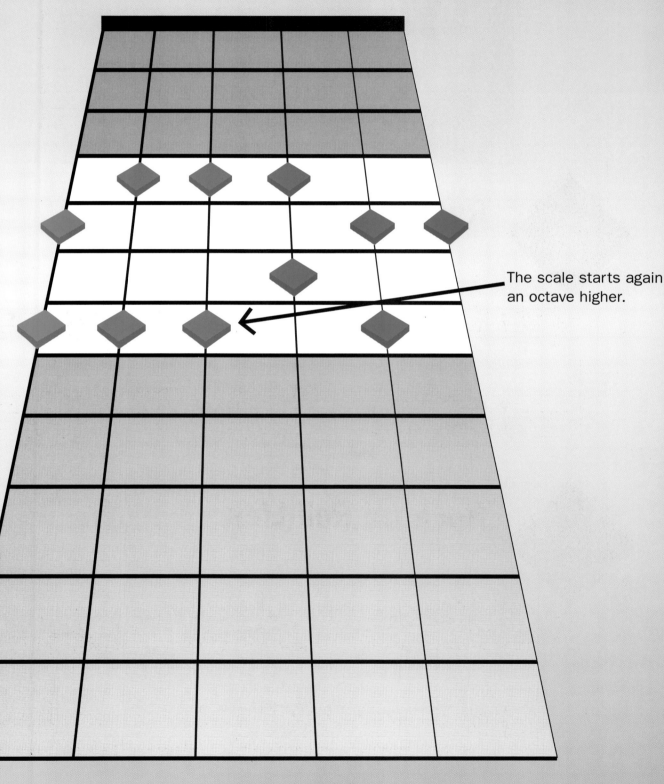

The scale starts again an octave higher.

'BOX PATTERN' LICKS

Rock Lick in A

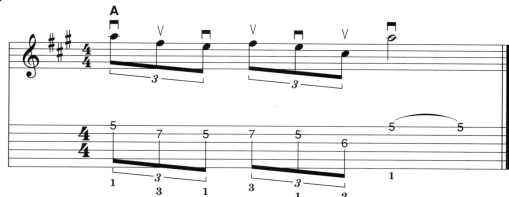

Country/Rock Lick

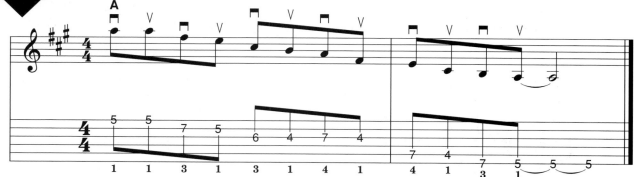

Rock 'n' Roll Lick

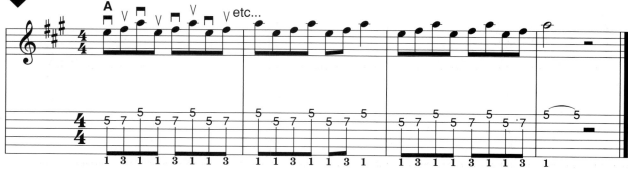

B Major Pentatonic

The notes for this scale are (starting at the 7th fret of the 6th string):

1,	2,	3,	5,	6.
B	C#	D#	F#	G# etc.

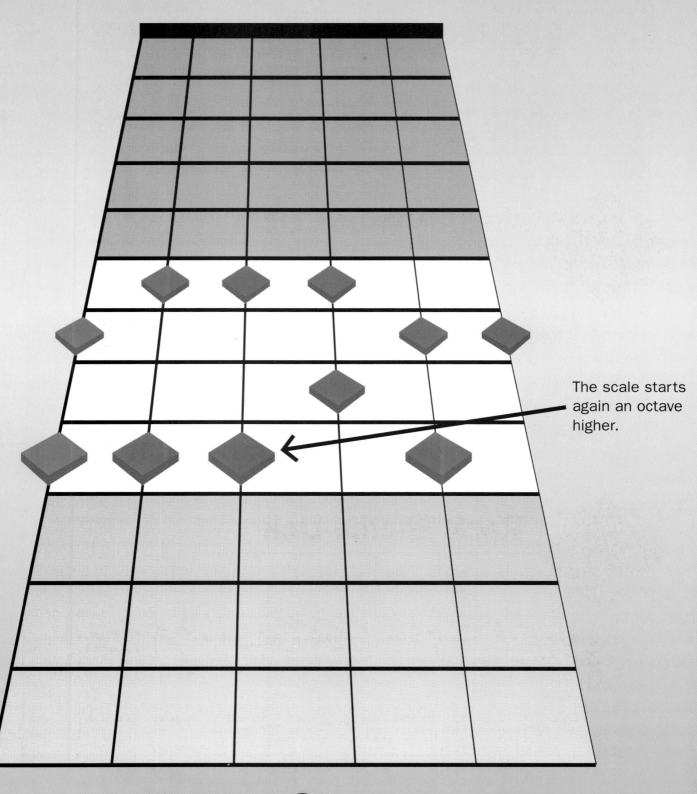

The scale starts again an octave higher.

'BOX PATTERN' LICKS

The following three licks are based on the B major pentatonic scale.

Turnaround Lick

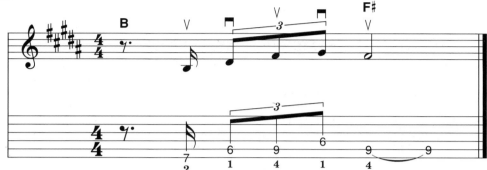

Outro Lick

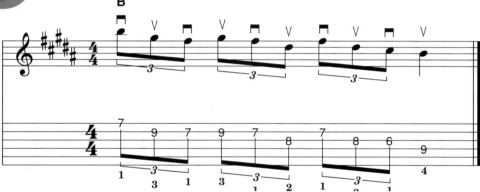

Rock Shuffle Lick

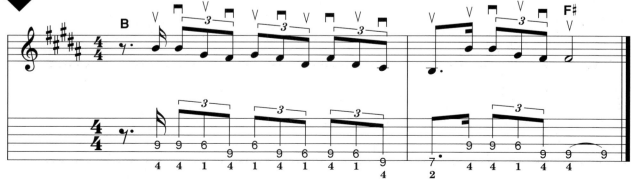

C Major Pentatonic

Here are the notes for the C major pentatonic scale (starting at the 8th fret of the 6th string). They are:

1,	2,	3,	5,	6.
C	D	E	G	A	etc.

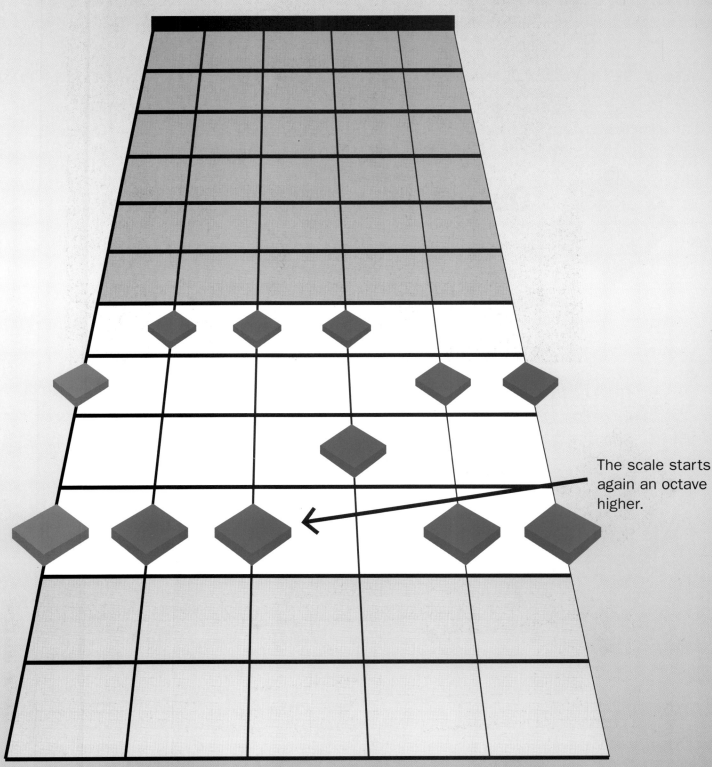

The scale starts again an octave higher.

'Box Pattern' Licks

Joe Satriani

15 Outro Lick

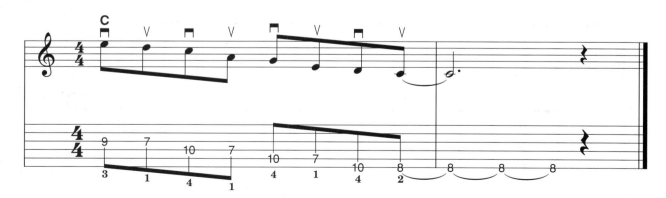

D Major Pentatonic

These are the notes for the D major pentatonic scale (starting at the 10th fret of the 6th string) :

1,	2,	3,	5,	6.
D	E	F#	A	B	etc.

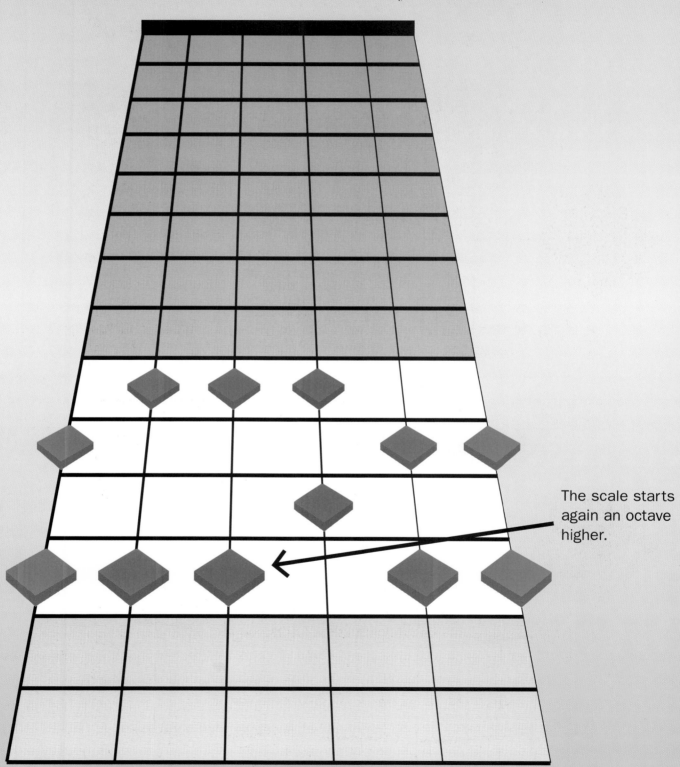

The scale starts again an octave higher.

'BOX PATTERN' LICKS

These three licks are based on the notes from the D major pentatonic scale.

Turnaround

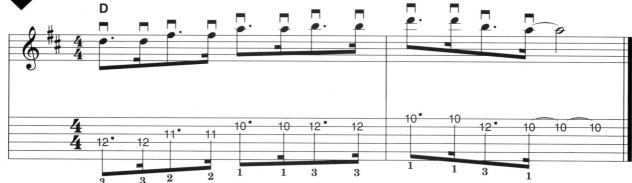

Outro Lick

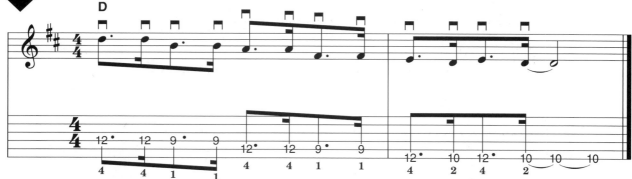

Lick in D

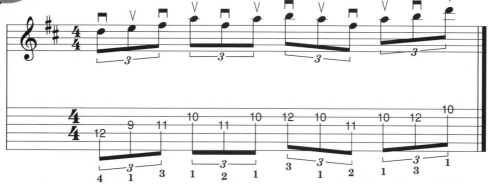

Breaking away from the Box Pattern

You don't want to always be confined to the box pattern. The examples on this page show how you can break away from this by using the slide technique (refer to the slide symbol on page 4).

First of all study the following box pattern lick.

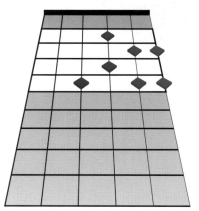

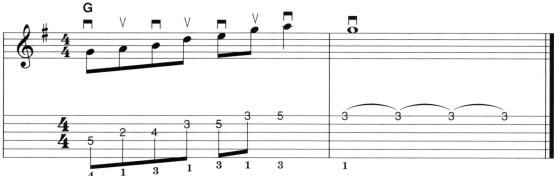

Now try this again, but this time when you get to the 5th note (5th fret of the 2nd string) slide your finger along to the 8th fret instead of the 3rd fret of the 1st string.
Here's the 'modified' lick.
(*Notice the last note has been shifted on to the 2nd string because of the slide).

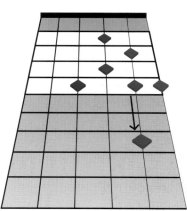

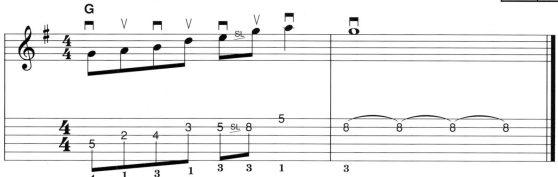

Rock Lick in E

Start this lick with a fast slide onto the 6th fret of the 3rd string. The slide doesn't really start from any particular fret (hence no note or fret number indicated).

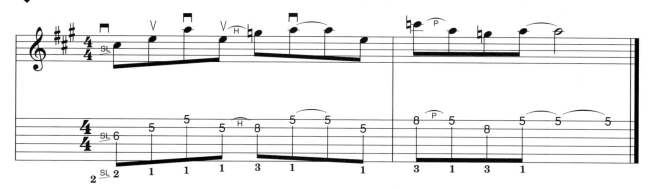

Rock Lick in A

An upward string bend is used at the beginning of this lick. Try reinforcing your 3rd finger with your 2nd finger as you bend the string up.

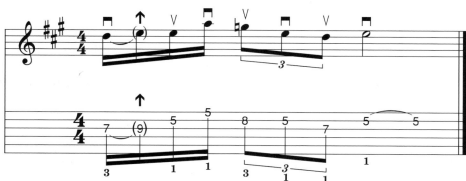

Turnaround

A turnaround is used at the end of a section of music (usually a 12-bar section) to turn you back to the start of the section again.

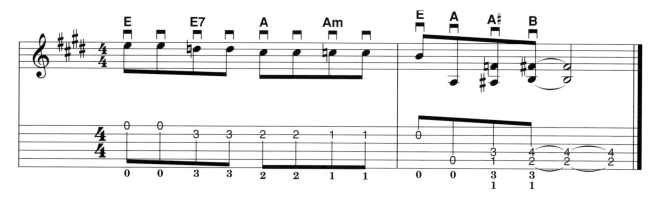

Pride & Glory

Rock Lick in E

Here's an exciting, twangy 50's style rock lick.

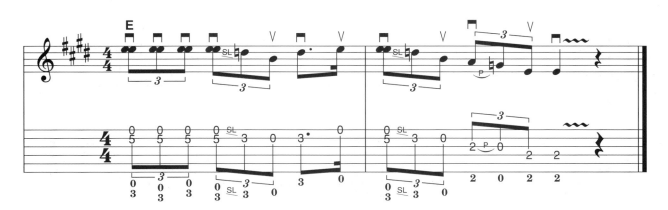

Rock/Blues Turnaround

This turnaround can be used in a rock or blues 12-bar.

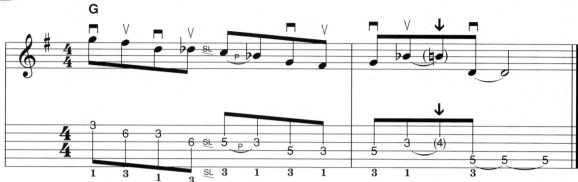

Outro Lick

You'll have to stretch your fingers a bit when going from the 4th to 5th note with the 3rd and 1st fingers. Although you may prefer to use your 4th finger instead of the 3rd.

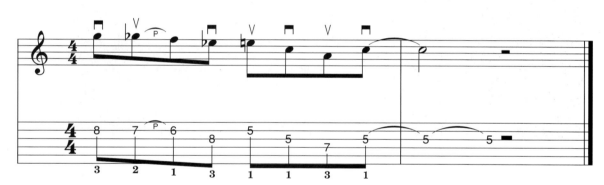

Roll Lick

The use of pull-offs together with the triplet notes help to give this a 'rolling' kind of sound. Work on this slowly to begin with.

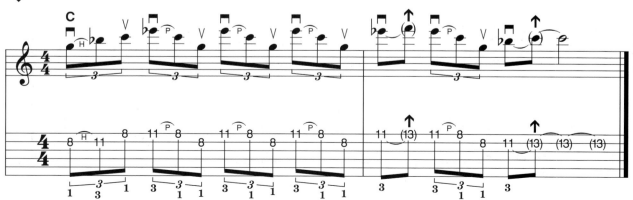

Rock Lick in E minor

Here's an easy descending lick which includes a couple of pull-offs.

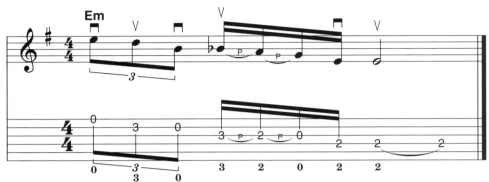

R 'n' B Lick

This Rhythm 'n' Blues lick has a 'straight' feel: 1 and 2 and 3 and 4 and etc.

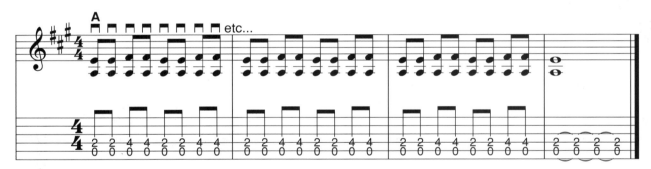

R 'n' B Shuffle Lick

This lick is similar to the one above but has a 'shuffle' feel:
1 and a 2 and a 3 and a 4 and a etc.

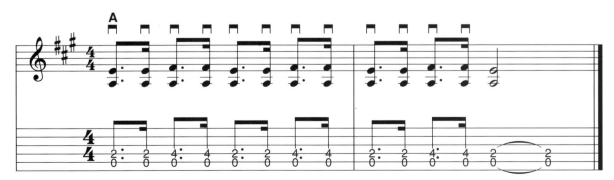

Intro Lick in C

The following lick is similiar to a Chuck Berry type of intro. Starting with two-note chords at the 8th fret and finishing with a two-note chord at the 11th fret.

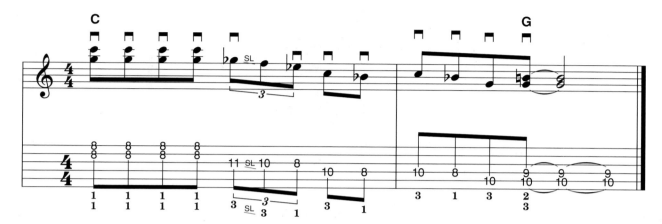

Rock Lick in C

This lick also has a Chuck Berry feel to it.

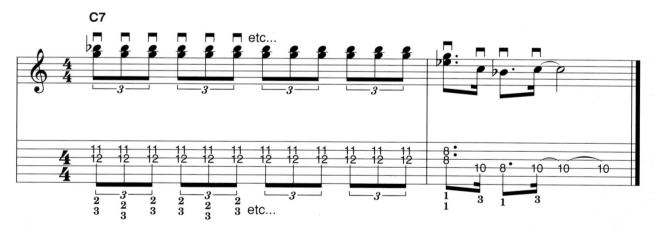

Rock Lick in G

The use of hammer-ons gives this lick a smooth rolling sort of sound.

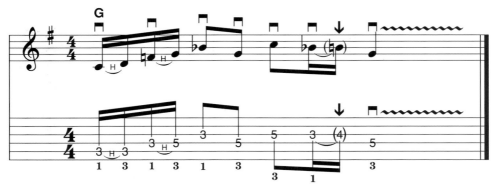

Outro in E

Here's an easy outro based on the E blues scale.

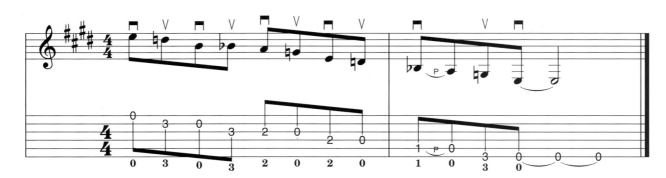

Intro in E

Here is one of the great classic intros which is still being used by guitar players to this day. This has a 'shuffle' feel to it.

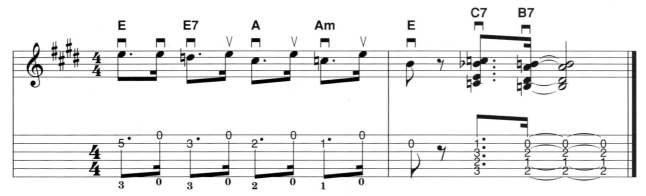

Be Bop Lick

This lick has a swing feel to it.

Rock Lick in D

A pre-bend is used at the start of this lick and is followed by a release, pull-off and upward string bend.

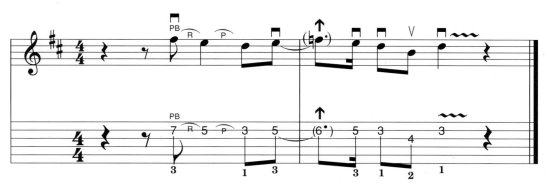

Rock Lick in D

A pre-bend followed by a release bend is used at the start of this lick as well.

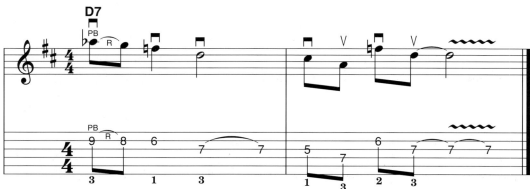

Heavy Metal Lick

Here's a great sounding heavy metal lick using power chords.

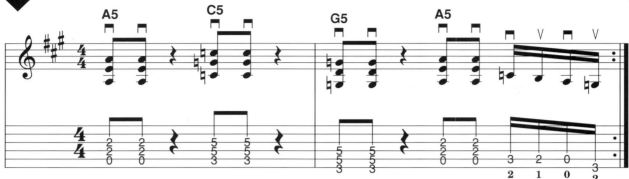

Intro Lick

This lick is played at the start of a song I wrote called 'Road to Glory' and it appears on the album 'Pluto Plus'.

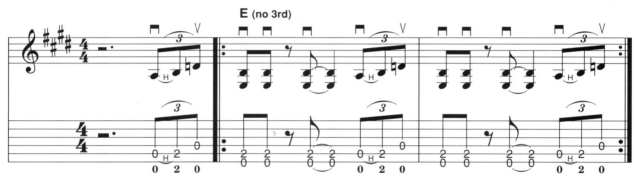

R 'n' B Lick

It's important that you accent the first and fourth beat when playing this rhythm blues lick.

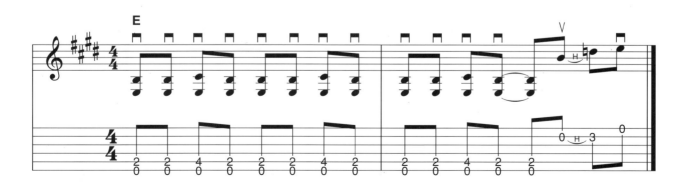

Roll Lick

Practise this lick slowly at first and then build up to a fairly fast speed.

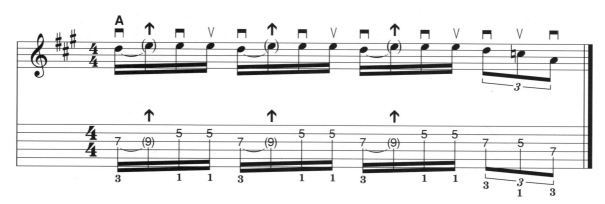

Country/Rock Lick

Combined pick and finger (hybrid picking) are used here and are very effective.
An *a* above a note represents the ring finger and the *m* represents the middle finger.

Rockabilly Lick

If you have an effects unit with echo on it, try setting it to a short delay (slapback) for that classic rockabilly sound.

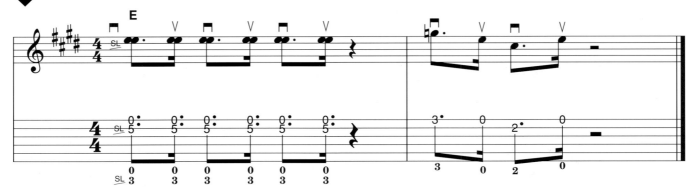

Rockabilly Lick

Bend the 8th fret note slightly for a more rocky sound.

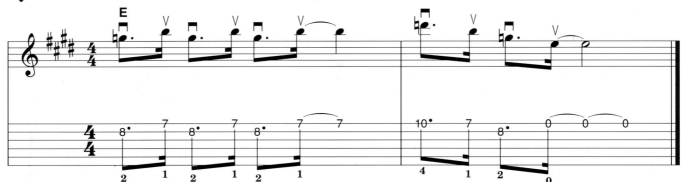

Rockabilly Lick

Use your pick and fingers for this hot lick or alternatively your thumb and fingers. Also try to get the slapback echo for greater effect.

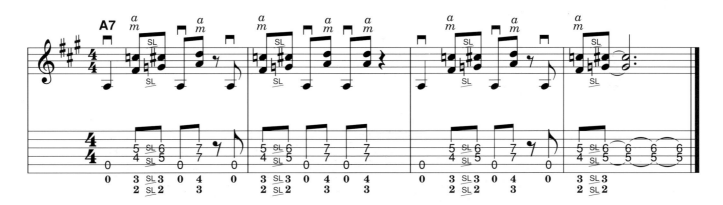

Outro in C

Start off with an upstroke for this lick. Notice the jazzy sounding C6/9 chord at the end.

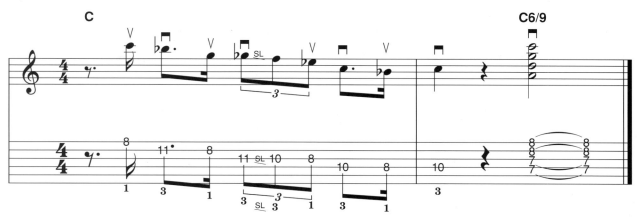

Country Rock Lick

Try to keep your L.H. 4th finger in place when bending the 2nd string up. You may need to work on this separately for a while before attempting the rest of the lick.

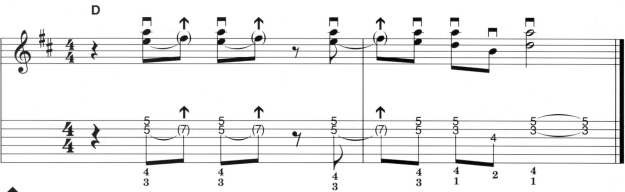

Flash Rock Lick

I've had this one in my 'Lick Repertoire' for as long as I can remember. It still sounds fresh today.

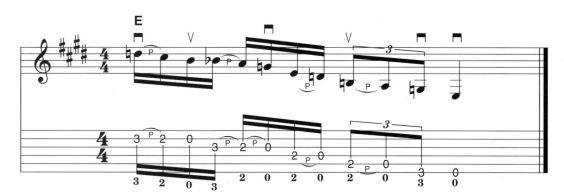

48 Turnaround

Here's a powerful turnaround lick useful in a Rock/Blues situation.

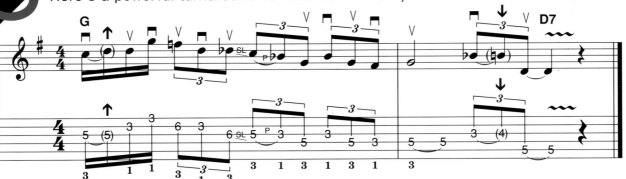

49 Rock 'n' Roll Lick

This is a 50's style Rock 'n' Roll lick.

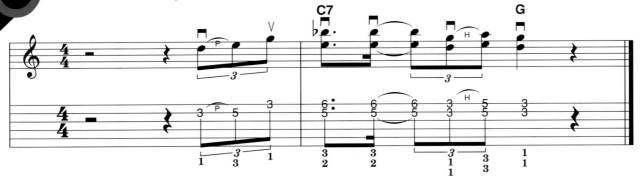

50 Heavy Metal Lick

Here's a powerful driving heavy metal lick. You may find it a bit difficult getting the hang of the rhythm. To get you started try counting like this on the first measure:

1 and a 2 and a 3 and a 4

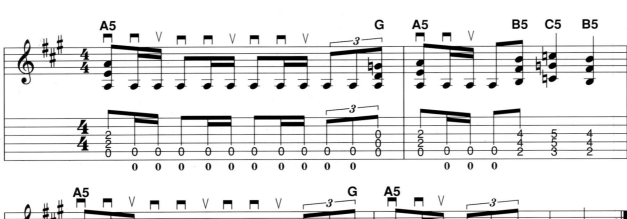

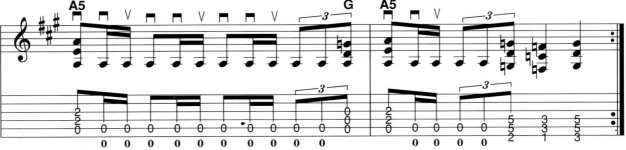